COUNTRY LOVE

Wise Publications
part of The Music Sales Group

London / New York / Paris / Sydney / Copenhagen / Berlin / Madrid / Tokyo

Published by
Wise Publications,
8/9 Frith Street, London W1D 3JB, England.

Exclusive distributors:
Music Sales Limited,
Distribution Centre, Newmarket Road, Bury St Edmunds,
Suffolk, IP33 3YB, England.

Music Sales Pty Limited,
120 Rothschild Avenue, Rosebery,
NSW 2018, Australia.

Order No. AM84625
ISBN 0-7119-2634-4
This book © Copyright 2004 by Wise Publications.

Music arrangements by Jack Long.
Music processed by Paul Ewers Music Design.

Printed in Malta by Interprint Limited.

www.musicsales.com

Your Guarantee of Quality:
As publishers, we strive to produce every book
to the highest commercial standards.

This book has been carefully designed to minimise
awkward page turns and to make playing from it a real pleasure.

Particular care has been given to specifying acid-free, neutral-sized paper
made from pulps which have not been elemental chlorine bleached.

This pulp is from farmed sustainable forests
and was produced with special regard for the environment.

Throughout, the printing and binding have been planned to ensure a sturdy,
attractive publication which should give years of enjoyment.

If your copy fails to meet our high standards, please inform us
and we will gladly replace it.

All I Have To Do Is Dream

Words & Music by Boudleaux Bryant

Always On My Mind

Words & Music by Wayne Thompson, Mark James & Johnny Christopher

7

Amazed

Words & Music by Marv Green, Aimee Mayo & Chris Lindsey

1. Ev - 'ry-time our eyes   meet,   this feel-in' in - side   me
(Verse 2 see block lyric)

Ev - 'ry lit - tle thing that you— do.

Ev - 'ry lit - tle thing that you— do,_____ I'm so in love_____ with you_

_____ it just keeps get-tin' bet - ter._____ I wan-na spend the rest of my_ life_

with you by my side _____ for- ev - er and ___ ev -

- er. _____ Ev - 'ry lit - tle thing that you do, ___

oh, _____ and ev - 'ry lit - tle thing that you ___ do,

ba - by I'm a - mazed ___ by

14

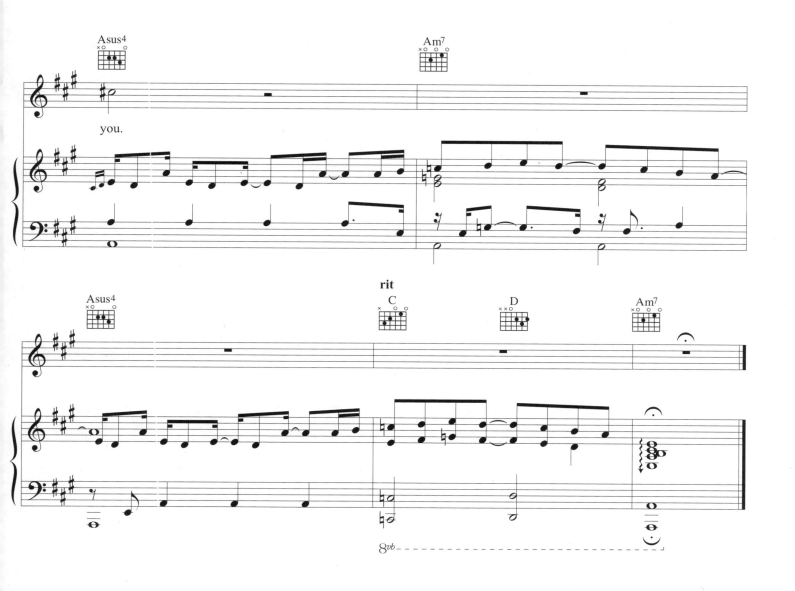

Verse 2:
The smell of your skin
The taste of your kiss
The way you whisper in the dark
Your hair all around me
Baby you surround me
Touch every place in my heart
Oh, it feels like the first time everytime
I wanna spend the whole night
In your eyes.

I don't know how you do what you do *etc.*

Angelina

Words & Music by Randy Scruggs & Billy Bob Thornton

1. I walked in-to an el-ev-at - or
2. They all said we'd nev-er make___ it:

and you walked in-to a wall.___
two cra-zy pan-thers on the prowl.___

You said you want-ed to be with___ me,___
They said we would on-ly fake___ it *(spoken)* for a while.

I nev - er dreamed___ I'd have it all.___
We just looked___ at them and growled.___

But some-thing changed that day in - side___ me,___
You were masked and tied___ and caught___ and wear - y:___

and I be - lieve it changed___ in - side you too. Yeah, An - ge - li -
but I said that's ok - ay,___ you could be a girl. An - ge - li -

18

Constant Craving

Words & Music by k.d. Lang & Ben Mink

Verse 2:
Maybe a great magnet pulls all souls towards truth
Or maybe it is life itself that feeds wisdom to its youth
And constant craving has always been.

Crazy

Words & Music by Willie Nelson

what in the world did I do.

Cra - zy _____ for think - ing that my love could hold you,

I'm cra - zy for try - in', cra - zy for cry - in' ____ and I'm

crazy for lov - in' you. you.

Dance The Night Away

Words & Music by Raul Malo

Here comes my hap - pi - ness a - gain,___

right back to where it should have ___ been,

'cause now she's gone and I am ___ free,

and she can't do a thing to ___ me.

I just wan - na dance the night a - way

28

with se - nor - it - as who can___ sway,

right now to - mor - row's look - in' bright,___

just like the sun - ny morn - in'___ light.

to Coda

31

right now to - mor - row's look - in' bright,__
(*second time instrumental*)

just like the sun - ny morn - in'____ light.

33

From A Distance

Words & Music by Julie Gold

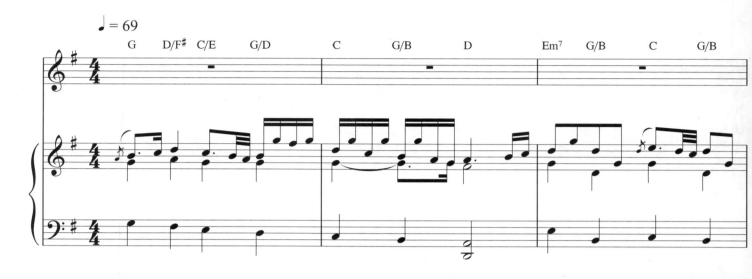

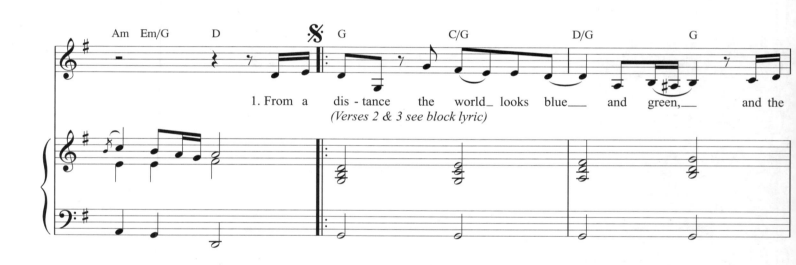

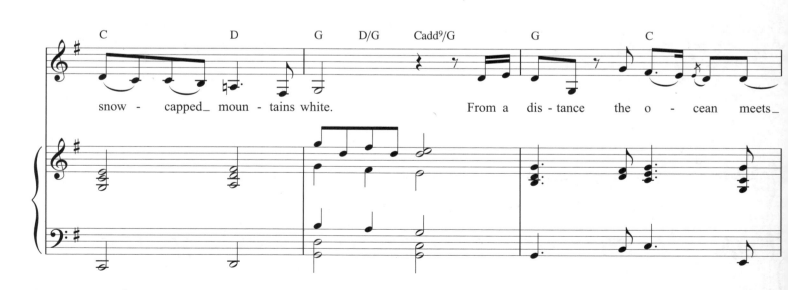

man. God_ is watch-ing us,____ God_ is watch-ing us,____ God_ is

watch-ing us from a dis-tance._

3. From a

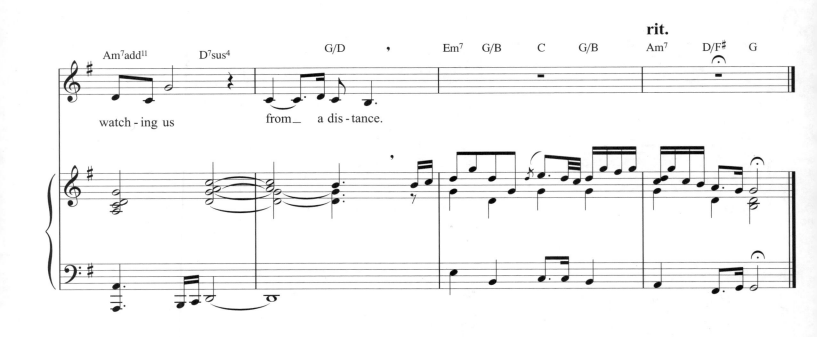

Verse 2:
From a distance we all have enough
And no one is in need.
And there are no guns, no bombs and no disease
No hungry mouths to feed.
For a moment we are instruments
Marching in a common band
Playing songs of hope, playing songs of peace
They're the songs of every man.

Verse 3:
From a distance you look like my friend
Even though we are at war.
From a distance I just cannot comprehend
What all this fighting is for.
From a distance there is harmony
And it echoes through the land
And it's the hope of hopes, it's the love of loves
It's the heart of every man.

From This Moment On

Words & Music by Shania Twain & R.J. Lange

be - cause of you. From this moment, as long as I live, I will love you, I pro-mise you this. There is no - thing I would-n't give from this mo - ment on. Uh - huh!

A Good Year For The Roses

Words & Music by Jerry Chesnut

least your lips ca - ressed them while you packed. Or the

lip print on a half - filled cup of cof - fee that you poured and did - n't

drink. But at least you thought you want - ed it, that's

so much more than I can say for me. What a good year for the

Verse 2:
After three full years of marriage
It's the first time that you haven't made the bed
I guess the reason we're not talkin'
There's so little left to say we haven't said
While a million thoughts go racing through my mind
I find I haven't said a word
From the bedroom the familiar sound
Of a baby's cryin' goes unheard.

Help Me Make It Through The Night

Words & Music by Kris Kristofferson

Moderato

Take the rib - bon from your hair,
Come and lay down by my side
Yes - ter - day is dead and gone

Shake it loose and let it fall,_____
Till the ear - ly morn - in light._____
And to - mor - row's out of sight,_____

Lay - in' soft up - on my skin,
All I'm tak - in' is your time.
And it's sad to be a - lone.

Like the shad - ows on the wall.

Help me make it thru the night.

Help me make it thru the night.

(To Fine)

To next strain

Fine

51

I don't care who's right or wrong, _____

I don't try to un-der-stand. _____

Let the dev-il take to-mor-row. _____

D.S. al Fine

Lord, to-night I need a friend. _____

How Do I Live

Words & Music by Diane Warren

1. How do I_____ get through one night with-out___ you?_____ If I had to live with-out___ you___ what kind of

(Verse 2 see block lyric)

Verse 2:
There'd be no sun in my sky
There would be no love in my life
There'd be no-one left for me
And I, oh baby, I don't know what I would do
I'd be lost if I lost you
If you ever leave
Baby you would take away everything real in my life.

And tell me now *etc.*

House Of Love

Words & Music by Greg Barnhill, Wally Wilson & Kenny Greenberg

1. You've been up___ all night   think-in' it was ov - er.
2. Now when the house is dark   and you're all a - lone in-side,
3. *(Instrumental)*

He's been out___ of sight,   at least for the mo - ment.
you gotta listen to your heart   and put a - way your foolish pride.

But when some-thing this strong,___ oh,___ gets a hold on___ you, the odds are
Though the storm is break - ing and thun - der shakes the walls,___
Though the storm is break - ing and thun - der shakes the walls,___

To Coda ⊕

E♭m7

nine - ty - nine___ to one_____ it's got a hold___ on___ him, too._____
there with a firm foun - da - tion___ ain't it nev - er, nev - er, never gon - na fall.
there with a firm foun - da - tion___ ain't it nev - er, nev - er, never gon - na fall.

G♭maj7/A♭

D♭

Well, I bet you a - ny a - mount of

Fm7

mo - ney he'll be com - in' back to___ you._____ Ooh,___

G♭maj7

B9

_____ I know___ there ain't no doubt a - bout it, some - times life is

D♭

61

I Recall A Gypsy Woman

Words & Music by Bob McDill & Allen Reynolds

Moderately, with an easy rhythm

where she held   me   to her   bo - som,____
while my ten - der   wife and   ba - bies____

just a boy____   of sev - en - teen.
slum - ber soft   -   ly in their beds.

I re - call_____   a gyp - sy wom - an,
Instrumental

sil - ver span   -   gles in her eyes;

iv - 'ry skin   a - gainst the moon - light____

and the taste____   of life's sweet wine.

D.S. and Fade

Soft breez - es blow_ wine

67

I Would've Loved You Anyway

Words & Music by Mary Danna & Troy Verges

if I'd 've had the strength to walk a - way,
but just to hold you close to me

if I'd 've known how this would hurt,
for a mo - ment in time.

I would -'ve loved you a - ny - way, I'd do it all the same

not a se - cond I would change, not a touch that I would trade.

69

-ing,___ you'd still have seen__ me run - ning straight in-to__ your__

D.S. al Coda   *Coda*

___ arms.___   break,

I would-'ve loved you a-ny - way.___

I would-'ve loved you a-ny - way.

rit.

If Tomorrow Never Comes

Words & Music by Garth Brooks & Kent Blazy

Verse 2:
'Cause I've lost loved ones in my life
Who never knew how much I loved them
Now I live with the regret
The natural feelings for them never were revealed
So I made a promise to myself
To say each day how much she means to me
And avoid that circumstance
Where there's no second chance
To tell her how I feel.

If tomorrow never comes *etc.*

Independence Day

Words & Music by Gretchen Peters

1. Well, she seemed__ al-right__ by dawn's__ ear-ly light,__ though she
(2.) word gets a-round in a small,__ small__ town;__ they
(3.) lit up the sky__ that Fourth__ of Ju-ly,__ by the

looked a lit-tle wor-ried and weak.__ She tried to pre-tend__ he was-n't
said he was a dan-ger-ous man.__ But Mom-ma was proud,__ and she stood__
time that the fire-men come.__ They just put out the flames__ and took__

It's Four In The Morning

Words & Music by Jerry Chesnut

Bright Swing Feel ♩ = 129

four in_____ the morn-ing_____ and once more____ the dawn-ing just
(2.) nev - er_____ de - serv'd her, God knows when____ I hurt her that's the

four in the morn - ing and once more the dawn - ing just

woke up the want - ing in me.   2. I

3. Last night I told her this time it's all o - ver, mak - ing
(4.) four in the morn - ing and once more the dawn - ing just

ten times I've told her good - bye.
woke up the want - ing in me. Wishing

Last night we broke up, this morn - ing I woke up, and for the
I'd nev - er met her, know - ing if I for - get her how

tenth time I'm chang - ing my mind. The
much bet - ter off she would be. The

84

85

Jolene

Words & Music by Dolly Parton

please don't take him ev - en though you___ can.___

Jo - lene.

Jo - lene.___

Repeat ad lib. to fade

90

Leavin'

Words & Music by Shelby Lynne

(Spoken) Well, I guess this is it, babe: reality has hit home hard. No need in puttin' it off any more, just turn away and let me walk out the door. You thought you had it all figured out; but, baby, you don't know what love's about. It's time for me to spend some time alone, I'm tired of trying to make this your happy home.

I'm leav - in'.

(Spoken) I know it's gonna be hard on you   once it really hits you that I'm gone.

I spent too much time trying to make things right,   when I really knew all along.   You'll be okay in time, baby,

but it won't be today.   As you walk around and try to find yourself take a look at the bed you made.

The Most Beautiful Girl

Words & Music by Rory Bourke, Billy Sherrill & Norris Wilson

97

99

Love Can Build A Bridge

Words & Music by John Jarvis, Paul Overstreet & Naomi Judd

2. I would

Don't you think it's time?

When we stand to-ge-ther it's our fi-nest hour. We can do

Right In Time

Words & Music by Lucinda Williams

The way___ you move   is right___ in   time,

it's right in time___   with___ me.___

rall.

III

Send Down An Angel

Words & Music by Allison Moorer & Doyle Primm

1. It's near-ly___ three___ a.____ m.,___ and still no___ sign___ of
2. Lord, I don't___ un-der-stand___ why I stand___ by___ my___
3. I'm not the___ pray-ing___ kind,___ but it can't___ hurt___ to

Songbird

Words & Music by Christine McVie

D.%. al Coda

2. To———— you——

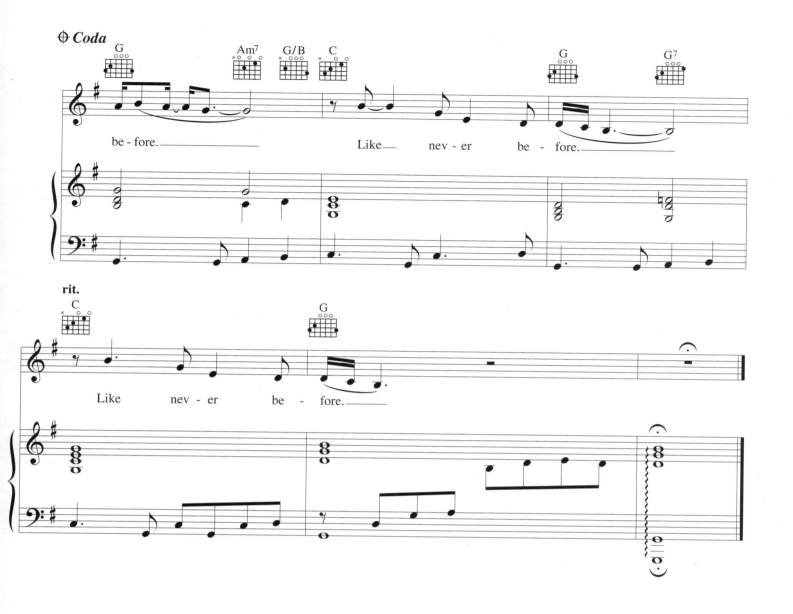

Verse 2:
To you I would give the world
To you I'd never be cold
'Cause I feel that when I'm with you
It's alright
I know it's right.

And the songbirds keep singing *etc.*

Swimming In Champagne

Words & Music by Richard Carpenter & Eric Heatherly

1. San - ta Mo - ni - ca sun - set___ de - cor - ates_ the sky,___ a
2. Float - ing on___ a white cloud with you in my arms,___ I

rose col - oured twi - light____ re - flects in your eyes.____
nev - er wan - na touch down____ gon - na live in the stars.____

As we touch,____ the hea - vens light up;____ and
And I don't wan-na wake up____ if this is a dream,____ 'cause this

we both know____ we're____ drown - ing in love.____ Feels like_ I'm
love is a rush____ when you're hold - ing me.____

swim - ming____ in cham - pagne,____ and

Talking In Your Sleep

Words & Music by Roger Cook & Bobby Wood

1. Three o' clock in the morn-ing and it looks like it's gon-na be a-noth-er
2. 3. Ba-by I'm be-ing fool-ish 'cos I have-n't heard you mention an-y-bo-dy's

sleep-less night I've been listen-ing to your dreams and get-tin' ve-ry low
name at all How I wish I could be sure it's me that turns you on

wonder-in' what I can do Each time you

close your eyes   I've heard it said that dream-ers nev-er lie

Bb7/D   Bb7   Bbm Cm7 Bbm/Db Bbm7/F Ab

CHORUS

You've been talk - in' in ___ your ___ sleep   sleep - in'   in your ___

Bbm7

___ dreams _____ with some ___ sweet lo - ver

Cm7   Db   Ab/Eb   Eb7

Hold - ing on ___ so _____ tight ___   lov - in' her the way__

Ab   Bbm7